MATH DRILLS

Written by **Shannon Keeley**

Illustrated by **Jackie Snider**

FlashKids

This book belongs to

_____

Colorization & Production by Creative Quotient – A Repro India Limited Enterprise

Flash Kids
A Division of Barnes & Noble
122 Fifth Avenue
New York, NY 10011

ISBN: 978-1-4114-9896-9

Please submit all inquiries to FlashKids@bn.com

Printed and bound in Canada

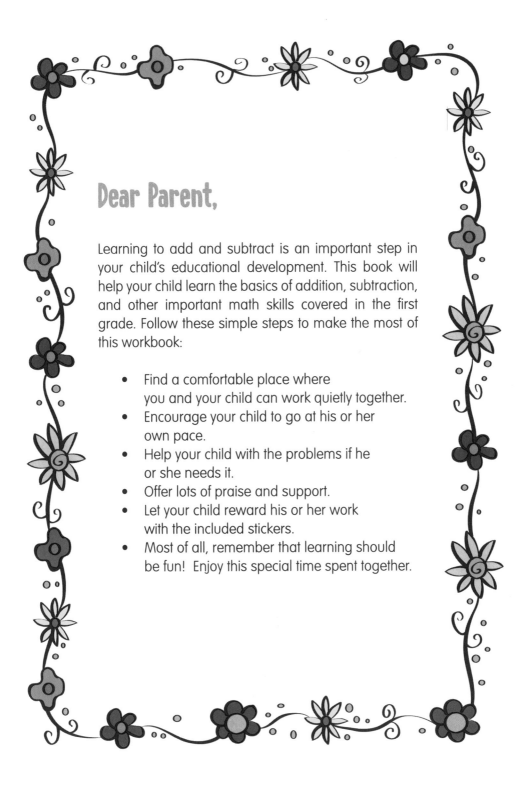

Dear Parent,

Learning to add and subtract is an important step in your child's educational development. This book will help your child learn the basics of addition, subtraction, and other important math skills covered in the first grade. Follow these simple steps to make the most of this workbook:

- Find a comfortable place where you and your child can work quietly together.
- Encourage your child to go at his or her own pace.
- Help your child with the problems if he or she needs it.
- Offer lots of praise and support.
- Let your child reward his or her work with the included stickers.
- Most of all, remember that learning should be fun! Enjoy this special time spent together.

Creature Count

Count each group of creatures. Write the number on the line.

1.  2.

_____   _____

3.   4.    5.

_____   _____   _____

Color the group with 1 creature **blue**.

Color the group with 2 creatures red.

Color the group with 3 creatures **black**.

Color the group with 4 creatures yellow.

Color the group with 5 creatures green.

Daisy Dots

Connect the dots from 1 to 30.

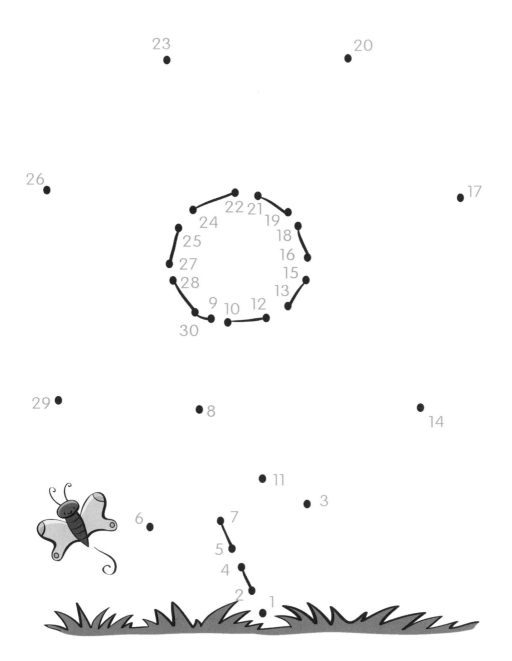

Petal Power

Count the petals on each flower. Write the number in the pot and the number word on the line. Use the letters inside the flowers to spell out the special message on page 7!

1.

2.

3.

_____

_____

_____

4.

5.

_____

_____

6.

_____

7.

_____

8.

_____

9.

_____

___ ___ ___ ___ ___ ___   ___ ___ ___

7   4   3   1   2   9   5   6   8

Seed Sums

Count the number of seeds in each group.

Write the number on the line.

Add the groups and write the sum in the flower.

1.

2.

3.

4.

How Many Spots?

Count the spots on each ladybug and write the number.

Add the spots and write the answer on the line.

1.

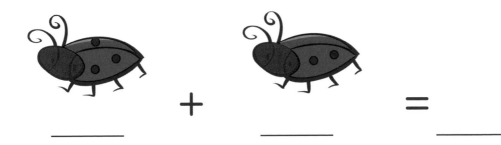

+ _____   = _____

2.

+ _____   = _____

3.

+ _____   = _____

Antsy Addition!

Draw a line to connect each problem to the correct answer.

1.

5 + 2

6

2.

6 + 0

8

3.

4 + 4

4

4.

3 + 1

7

Leafy Lesson

Add and write the sum. Color the leaves with sums of 2, 4, or 6.

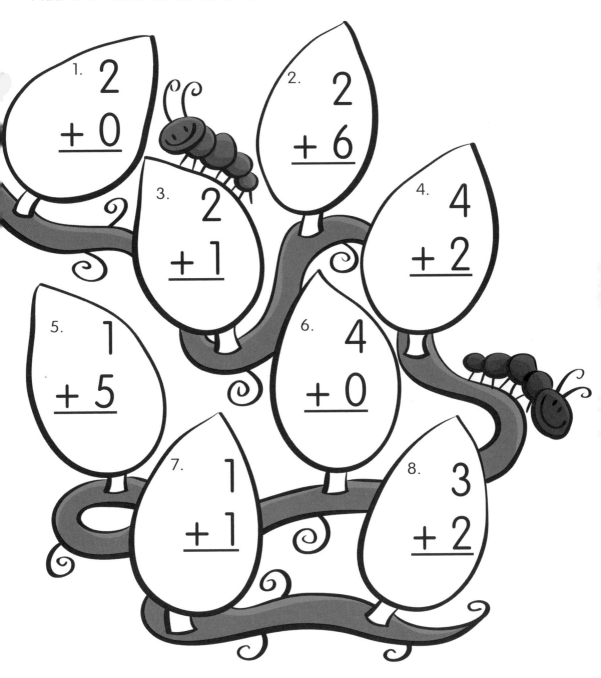

1. 2
   + 0
   ———

2. 2
   + 6
   ———

3. 2
   + 1
   ———

4. 4
   + 2
   ———

5. 1
   + 5
   ———

6. 4
   + 0
   ———

7. 1
   + 1
   ———

8. 3
   + 2
   ———

Flower Power

Add and write the sum on the line.

Find each sum below and write the letter to answer the riddle.

1. $3 + 4 = $ _____ **F**

2. $1 + 7 = $ _____ **S**

3. $0 + 1 = $ _____ **L**

4. $5 + 1 = $ _____ **N**

5. $8 + 1 = $ _____ **R**

6. $2 + 2 = $ _____ **E**

7. $3 + 0 = $ _____ **U**

8. $1 + 1 = $ _____ **W**

9. $5 + 0 = $ _____ **O**

Which flower is the brightest in the garden?

_____ _____ _____ _____ _____ _____ _____ _____ _____
8   3   6   7   1   5   2   4   9

Hop to It!

Add to help the grasshopper find the flower.

Write the sum in each stone.

1.
$$3$$
$$+2$$

2.
$$5$$
$$+4$$

3.
$$4$$
$$+2$$

4.
$$7$$
$$+0$$

5.
$$8$$
$$+1$$

6.
$$3$$
$$+7$$

7.
$$8$$
$$+0$$

8.
$$1$$
$$+1$$

Garden Graph

The graph shows how many of each flower are in the garden.
Use the graph to solve the problems.

rose	 🌹 🌹 🌹
daisy	 🌼 🌼 🌼 🌼
tulip	 🌷 🌷 🌷 🌷 🌷
lily	 🌺 🌺

1. How many roses and daisies in all?

_____ + _____ = _____

2. How many lilies and roses altogether?

_____ + _____ = _____

3. How many tulips and daisies in all?

_____ + _____ = _____

4. How many lilies and tulips altogether?

_____ + _____ = _____

Butterfly Fun

Add. Use the code to color the parts of the butterfly.

6 = blue   7 = red   8 = yellow   9 = brown

1.
4
+ 2

7.
5
+ 4

4.
3
+ 3

2.
6
+ 2

8.
6
+ 3

5.
7
+ 1

3.
4
+ 3

6.
5
+ 2

Picking Flowers

Read the sentences and solve the problems.
Show your work.

1. Jake picked 4 daisies and 2 roses. How many flowers did he pick in all? _____

2. Emily, David, Josh, and Amy each picked one flower. How many flowers did they pick in all?

_____

3. Nobody picked the tulip! There were 3 ants and 5 snails on the tulip. How many bugs were on the tulip altogether?_____

4. Julie picked a flower with 4 petals. Jane picked a flower with 5 petals. How many petals in all were on their flowers? _____

Terrific Tens

Solve the problems. If the sum equals 10, color the section green.

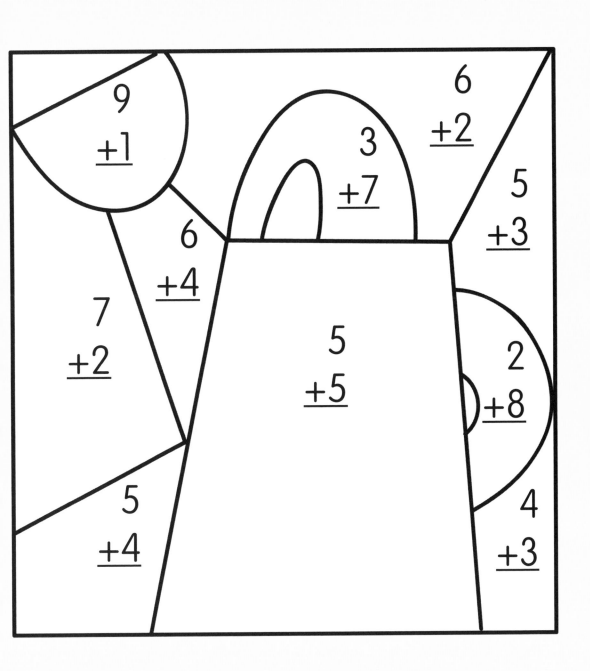

$$9 \atop {+1}$$

$$6 \atop {+2}$$

$$3 \atop {+7}$$

$$5 \atop {+3}$$

$$6 \atop {+4}$$

$$7 \atop {+2}$$

$$5 \atop {+5}$$

$$2 \atop {+8}$$

$$5 \atop {+4}$$

$$4 \atop {+3}$$

Tool Time

Count the total number of garden tools in each box and write the number on the first line. Then count the tools with an X through them and write that number on the second line. Subtract and write the difference on the third line.

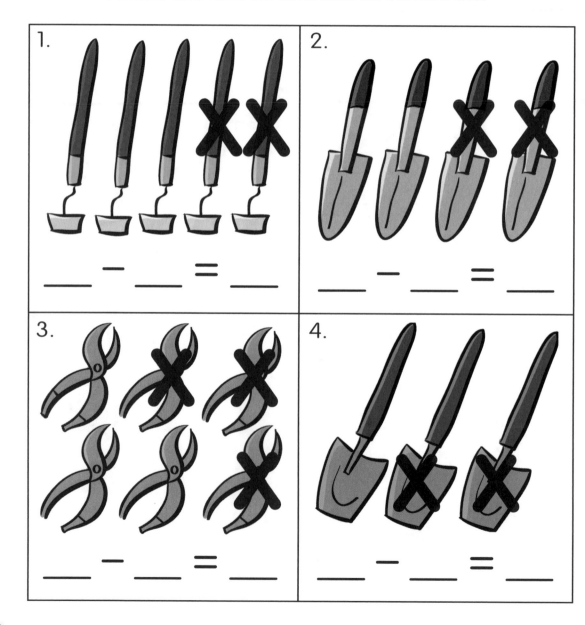

Watch Out Below!

Count the total pieces of fruit in each box and write the number on the
first line. Then count the pieces of falling fruit and write the number on
the second line. How many pieces are left on the tree?
Write the difference on the third line.

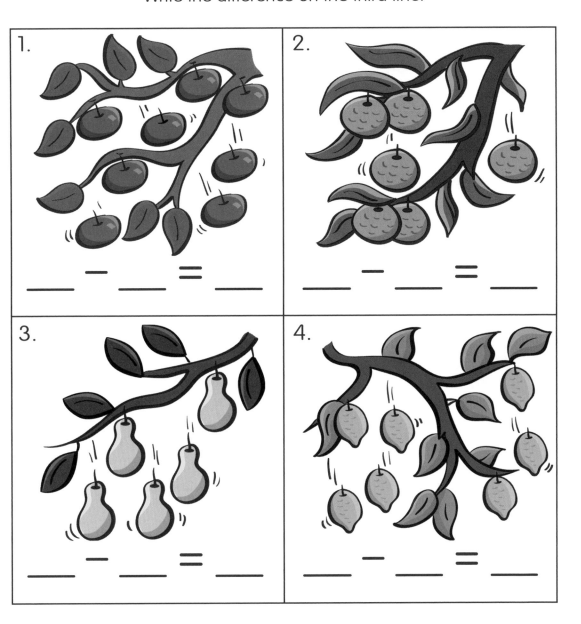

1.

2.

3.

4.

Buggy Races

Solve each problem. Color the answers on the path as you go.

Which bug wins the race?

START

6

1

5

3

8

2

4

7

FINISH

1. $9 - 3 =$ _____

2. $8 - 7 =$ _____

3. $5 - 2 =$ _____

4. $9 - 4 =$ _____

5. $6 - 4 =$ _____

6. $9 - 1 =$ _____

7. $8 - 4 =$ _____

8. $9 - 2 =$ _____

Ant March Math

Find the difference and write it inside the crumb.

1. 7
 − 4

2. 3
 − 2

3. 8
 − 6

4. 9
 − 3

5. 5
 − 5

6. 7
 − 2

7. 8
 − 4

8. 6
 − 5

Riddle Time

Subtract the numbers.

Use the answers to solve the riddle.

1. $8 - 2 =$ ___	R
2. $7 - 2 =$ ___	A
3. $5 - 1 =$ ___	D
4. $7 - 6 =$ ___	Y
5. $6 - 3 =$ ___	O
6. $9 - 0 =$ ___	F
7. $8 - 8 =$ ___	L
8. $4 - 2 =$ ___	G
9. $8 - 1 =$ ___	N

What insect name sounds like it can breathe fire?

___ ___ ___ ___ ___ ___ ___ ___ ___
4   6   5   2   3   7   9   0   1

Potted Problems

Subtract and write the answer inside the pot.

1.  $8 - 2$

2.  $6 - 4$

3.  $9 - 5$

4.  $5 - 0$

5.  $7 - 3$

6.  $8 - 5$

7.  $2 - 2$

8.  $3 - 2$

Subtraction Vine

Solve the problems and fill in the missing numbers
on the subtraction vine.

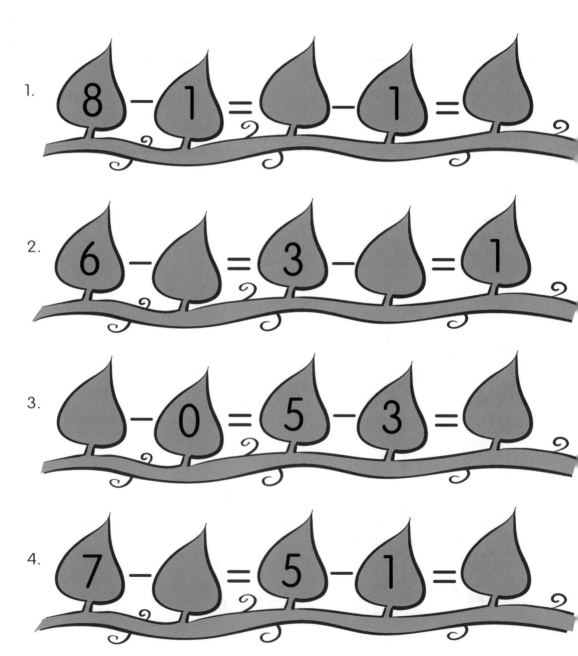

1. $8 - 1 = - 1 = $

2. $6 - = 3 - = 1$

3. $ - 0 = 5 - 3 = $

4. $7 - = 5 - 1 = $

Missing Petals

Each flower started out with 10 petals, but some of the petals fell off!

How many petals are missing?

Count the petals on each flower and fill in the missing number.

1. 10
    —
    =
    —
    7

2. 10
    —
    =
    —
    4

3. 10
    —
    =
    —
    2
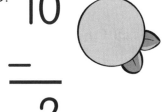

4. 10
    —
    =
    —
    8

5. 10
    —
    =
    —
    5

6. 10
    —
    =
    —
    3

7. 10
    —
    =
    —
    6

8. 10
    —
    =
    —
    9

Bug Tales

Read the sentences and solve the problems. Show your work.

1. There were 8 bees on the flower, but 4 flew away. How many bees were left on the flower? _____

2. Jeff saw 5 worms wiggling in the grass. He picked up 3 worms and held them in his hand. How many worms were left in the grass? _____

3. On the picnic table, there were 6 ants looking for food. Half of the ants went for walk in the grass. How many ants were left on the table? _____

When to Water

At what time should each plant be watered?

Read the clocks and write the time on the pot.

1. ___ : ___ ___

2. ___ : ___ ___

3. ___ : ___ ___

4. ___ : ___ ___

Sunny Solutions

Draw a line to connect each problem to the correct answer.

1. 5 + 4

2. 6 − 2

3. 3 + 2

4. 4 − 1

5. 7 + 1

3

5

8

9

4

Winged Pairs

Solve each pair of problems.

If both problems have the same answer, color the butterfly wings.

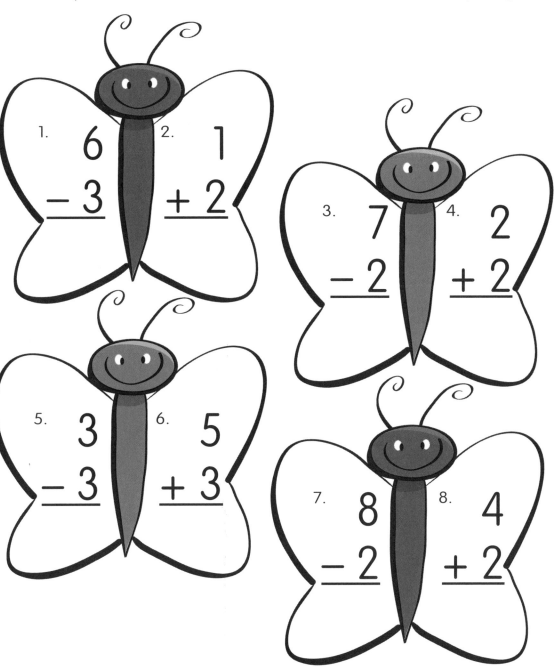

1. 6
  − 3

2. 1
  + 2

3. 7
  − 2

4. 2
  + 2

5. 3
  − 3

6. 5
  + 3

7. 8
  − 2

8. 4
  + 2

Garden Surprise

Solve the problems. If the answer is even, color the section green.

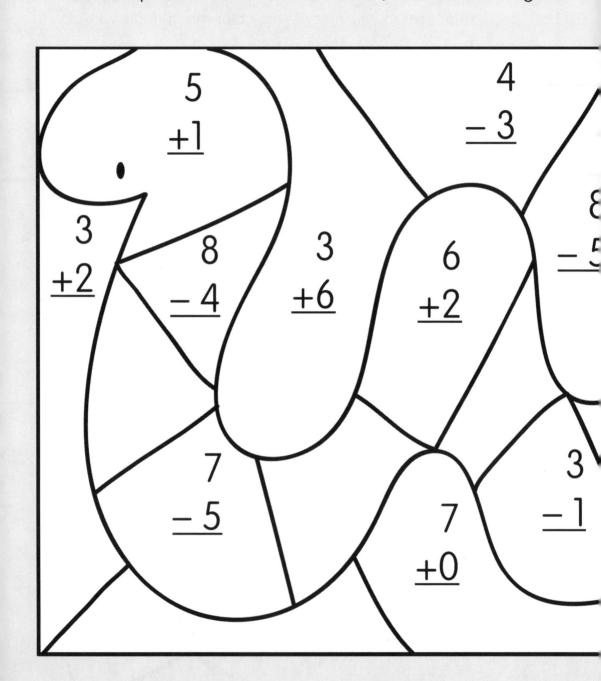

5
+1

4
− 3

3
+2

8
− 4

3
+6

6
+2

8
− 5

7
− 5

7
+0

3
− 1

Patch of Problems

Solve the problems.

1. $8 - 3 =$ _____

2. $4 + 1 =$ _____

3. $7 - 4 =$ _____

4. $3 + 2 =$ _____

5. $3 + 4 =$ _____

6. $9 - 2 =$ _____

7. $3 + 3 =$ _____

In the Orchard

Read the sentences. Add or subtract to solve the problems.
Show your work.

1. Jim picked 5 strawberries and 2 blueberries.
   How many berries did he have altogether?

   _____

2. The plum tree had 4 plums on Monday. Later
   that week, 4 more plums started growing on the
   same tree branch. How many plums in total were
   on the branch that week? _____

3. There were 6 apples on the apple tree. Mary picked
   apple and Jane picked 1, too. How
   many apples were left?

   _____

Hose Down!

Add or subtract to reach the end of each hose.

1. $6 - \underline{} = 3 + \underline{} = 5$

2. $\underline{} - 4 = 4 - 2 = \underline{}$

3. $3 + 6 = \underline{} - \underline{} = 4$

4. $5 + 2 = \underline{} - 1 = $

Threes and Trees

Add together all three numbers and write the sum.

1.
$$\begin{array}{r} 4 \\ 2 \\ +\,3 \\ \hline \end{array}$$

2.
$$\begin{array}{r} 3 \\ 1 \\ +\,2 \\ \hline \end{array}$$

3.
$$\begin{array}{r} 5 \\ 2 \\ +\,1 \\ \hline \end{array}$$

4.
$$\begin{array}{r} 2 \\ 2 \\ +\,2 \\ \hline \end{array}$$

5.
$$\begin{array}{r} 4 \\ 1 \\ +\,2 \\ \hline \end{array}$$

6.
$$\begin{array}{r} 7 \\ 1 \\ +\,0 \\ \hline \end{array}$$

Clever Clovers

Add together the three numbers in the clover leaves.

1.
 ____

2.
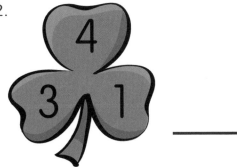 ____

3.
 ____

4.
 ____

5.
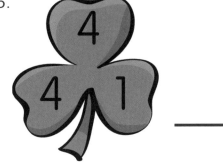 ____

6.
 ____

Mushroom Math

Add the numbers. Write each answer inside the stem.

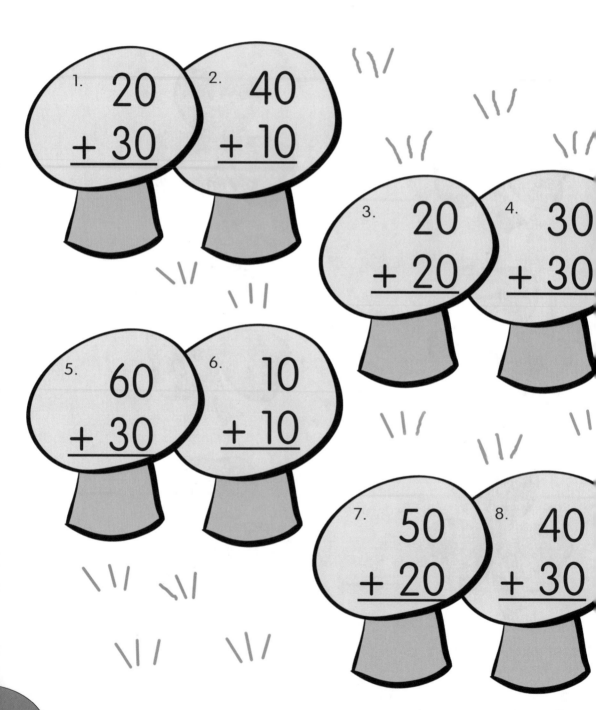

1. 20
+ 30

2. 40
+ 10

3. 20
+ 20

4. 30
+ 30

5. 60
+ 30

6. 10
+ 10

7. 50
+ 20

8. 40
+ 30

Subtraction Puzzle

First, subtract the numbers going across.

Then subtract the numbers going down. Finally, subtract your answers down and across. Write the answer in the shaded box.

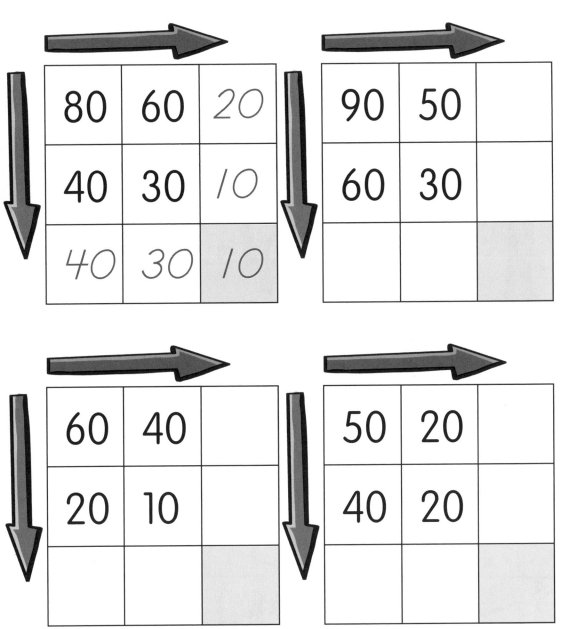

80	60	20
40	30	10
40	30	10

90	50	
60	30	

60	40	
20	10	

50	20	
40	20	

Grass Class

Add the numbers on each blade of grass.

1. 13
+ 4

3. 11
+ 5

5. 20
+ 7

7. 22
+ 7

2. 24
+ 4

4. 32
+ 6

6. 35
+ 4

8. 41
+ 6

Tree Riddle

Add the numbers.
Use the letter next to each sum to
break the code and solve the riddle.

1. 14
+ 3
U =

2. 30
+ 7
T =

3. 26
+ 2
N =

4. 23
+ 4
O =

5. 15
+ 4
R =

6. 31
+ 7
N =

7. 12
+ 6
W =

8. 37
+ 2
K =

A tree doesn't need a suitcase

because it has its

___ ___ ___   ___ ___ ___ ___ ___
27 18 28   37 19 17 38 39

Caterpillar Capers

Read the sentences and solve the problems. Show your work.

1. The hungry caterpillar ate 10 leaves one week. The next week it ate only 4 leaves. How many leaves did it eat in all? _____

2. There were 4 caterpillars on the tree branch. Then, 11 more caterpillars crawled onto the same branch. How many caterpillars are on the branch now? _____

3. The caterpillar crawled 6 feet in the morning and 12 feet in the afternoon. How many feet did it crawl in total? _____

4. Before becoming a butterfly, the caterpillar ate leaves for 7 days and stayed in a cocoon for 10 days. How many days did it take in all for the caterpillar to turn into a butterfly? _____

Veggies for Sale

Circle the coins you need to buy each vegetable.

 1. 27¢

 2. 51¢

 3. 40¢

 4. 42¢

Lily Leap

Solve the problems and help the frog jump to next lily pad.

1. 14
   − 3

2. 24
   − 4

3. 19
   − 7

4. 26
   − 3

5. 35
   − 4

6. 18
   − 7

7. 25
   − 1

8. 39
   − 4

Garden Gates

Subtract the numbers.

1. $27 - 3$

2. $13 - 2$

3. $39 - 6$

4. $44 - 2$

5. $46 - 6$

6. $36 - 5$

7. $17 - 3$

8. $30 - 0$

Trail of Twos

Find the trail whose numbers count by twos.

Circle the bunch of carrots at the end of the correct trail.

Hive of Fives

Count by fives to fill in the missing numbers in the beehive.

5   *10*

15   ___   ___

___   35   ___

45   ___   ___   60

65   ___   75   ___

Ready, Set, Grow

Solve each problem by adding or subtracting.
Draw a line to the answer.

1. 54 − 2

2. 16 + 3

3. 36 − 4

4. 23 + 5

5. 48 − 5

32

43

28

19

52

Garden Growth

Read the sentences and solve the problems. Show your work.

1. There were 14 daisies growing in the garden. Then 5 more daisies bloomed. How many daisies are there now? _____

2. The garden had 18 weeds growing in it. The gardener pulled out 8 weeds. How many weeds are left? _____

3. The fern plant was 22 inches at the beginning of the summer. It grew 6 more inches during that summer. How many inches tall was it at the end of the summer? _____

4. The rosebush had 29 thorns on it. The gardener took off 8 thorns. How many thorns are still on the bush? _____

Raindrops

Solve the problem inside each raindrop.

1.
$$16 \\ +22$$

2.
$$24 \\ +62$$

3.
$$33 \\ +16$$

4.
$$64 \\ +21$$

5.
$$40 \\ +19$$

6.
$$29 \\ +10$$

7.
$$44 \\ +22$$

8.
$$53 \\ +24$$

Add It Up!

Add the numbers. Use the letter next to each sum
to break the code and read the sign.

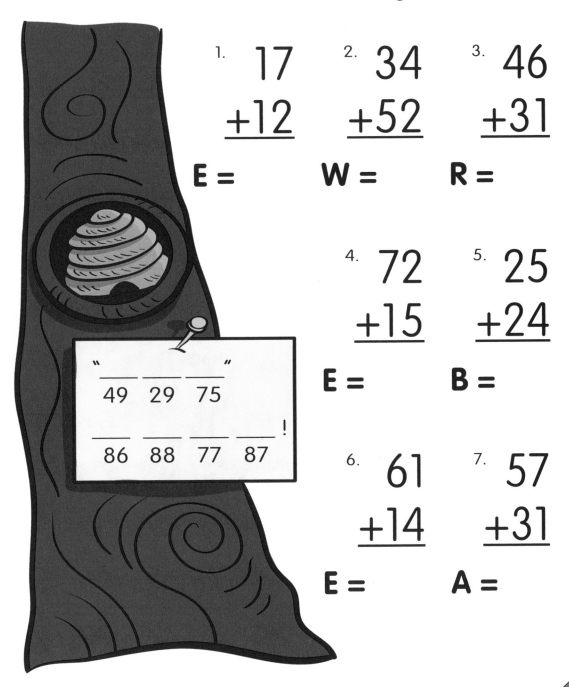

1. 17
    +12

    E =

2. 34
    +52

    W =

3. 46
    +31

    R =

4. 72
    +15

    E =

5. 25
    +24

    B =

6. 61
    +14

    E =

7. 57
    +31

    A =

"___ ___ ___"
 49   29   75

___ ___ ___ ___ !
86   88   77   87

Maze of Tens

Count by tens to find a path through the maze.

10   20   30

50   30   50   40

40

90   60   60   70

70   30

80

90   100

Toadstool Sums

Add. Follow the code to color the picture.

50 = green   20 = brown   40 = black

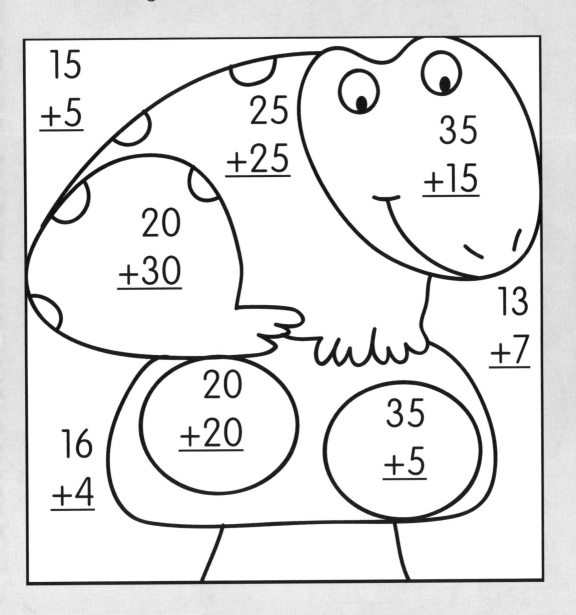

15
+5

25
+25

35
+15

20
+30

13
+7

20
+20

35
+5

16
+4

Pumpkin Patch

Subtract to find the difference.

1. 54
   − 12

2. 32
   − 20

3. 14
   − 11

4. 27
   − 13

5. 39
   − 16

6. 46
   − 33

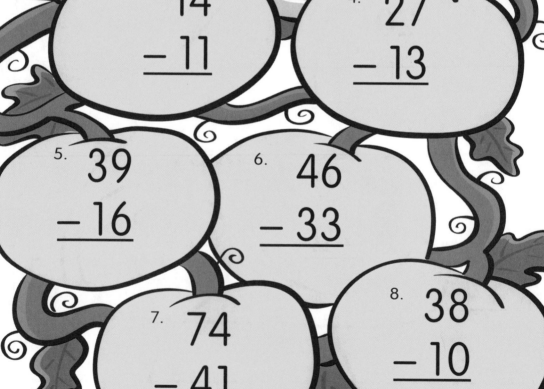

7. 74
   − 41

8. 38
   − 10

Bloom Zoom

Solve each problem by subtracting. Color the answers on the paths
as you go to find out which flower blooms first.

START

13		11
4		31
23		7
44		12

FINISH

1. $23 - 12 =$ _____

2. $34 - 21 =$ _____

3. $26 - 22 =$ _____

4. $57 - 26 =$ _____

5. $46 - 23 =$ _____

6. $17 - 10 =$ _____

7. $64 - 52 =$ _____

8. $55 - 11 =$ _____

Lots of Pots

Subtract. If the difference is 20 or more, color the pot red.

If the difference is less than 20, color the pot blue.

1.
$$66 - 32$$

2.
$$50 - 30$$

3.
$$16 - 15$$

4.
$$41 - 20$$

5.
$$46 - 24$$

6.
$$29 - 17$$

7.
$$36 - 21$$

8.
$$18 - 10$$

The Rose Garden

The gardener counted the number of roses growing in the garden for five weeks. Use the gardener's chart to solve the problems.

Week	1	2	3	4	5
Number of roses	12	15	22	26	30

1. How many new roses grew from week 2 to week 3? _____

2. How many new roses grew between week 1 and week 5? _____

3. What is the greatest number of new roses that grew during one week? _____

4. What is the least number of new roses that grew during one week? _____

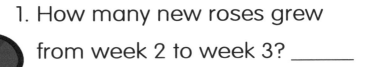

Branching Out

Add or subtract to solve the problems.

1.
$$\begin{array}{r} 23 \\ -13 \\ \hline \end{array}$$

2.
$$\begin{array}{r} 32 \\ +42 \\ \hline \end{array}$$

3.
$$\begin{array}{r} 50 \\ -30 \\ \hline \end{array}$$

4.
$$\begin{array}{r} 34 \\ +25 \\ \hline \end{array}$$

5.
$$\begin{array}{r} 85 \\ -80 \\ \hline \end{array}$$

6.
$$\begin{array}{r} 31 \\ +24 \\ \hline \end{array}$$

Bumblebee Fun

Solve the problems. If the answer is greater than 50, color the section yellow. If the answer is less than 50, color the section black.

1. $64 - 40 =$ _____
2. $61 - 10 =$ _____
3. $34 + 14 =$ _____
4. $46 + 13 =$ _____
5. $55 - 24 =$ _____
6. $82 - 21 =$ _____

The Birdhouse

Add or subtract
to solve the problems.

1. $$\begin{array}{r} 42 \\ -32 \\ \hline \end{array}$$

2. $$\begin{array}{r} 61 \\ +13 \\ \hline \end{array}$$

3. $$\begin{array}{r} 45 \\ -25 \\ \hline \end{array}$$

4. $$\begin{array}{r} 31 \\ +24 \\ \hline \end{array}$$

5. $$\begin{array}{r} 75 \\ -50 \\ \hline \end{array}$$

6. $$\begin{array}{r} 46 \\ +43 \\ \hline \end{array}$$

7. $$\begin{array}{r} 87 \\ -46 \\ \hline \end{array}$$

8. $$\begin{array}{r} 53 \\ +25 \\ \hline \end{array}$$

Rainy Arithmetic

Solve the problems.

1. $\begin{array}{r} 82 \\ -41 \\ \hline \end{array}$

2. $\begin{array}{r} 50 \\ +29 \\ \hline \end{array}$

3. $\begin{array}{r} 33 \\ -12 \\ \hline \end{array}$

4. $\begin{array}{r} 40 \\ +15 \\ \hline \end{array}$

5. $\begin{array}{r} 62 \\ -30 \\ \hline \end{array}$

6. $\begin{array}{r} 13 \\ +64 \\ \hline \end{array}$

7. $\begin{array}{r} 29 \\ -27 \\ \hline \end{array}$

8. $\begin{array}{r} 46 \\ +10 \\ \hline \end{array}$

Home Sweet Home

It took 30 minutes for the honeybee to fly from flower to flower.
Write the time when the bee landed on each flower.

12 : 0 0

1.
____ : _____

2.
____ : _____

3.
____ : _____

4.
____ : _____

5.
____ : _____

HOME

6. It took the bee an hour to fly from the last flower to the hive.
What time did the bee arrive at home? ____ : ____ ____

Garden Sale!

Count the coins and write the amount for each item from the garden.

Write the < or > symbol to show which item costs more.

Answer Key

Page 4
1. 4
2. 3
3. 5
4. 2
5. 1

Page 5

Pages 6-7
1. 5 five
2. 8 eight
3. 6 six
4. 1 one
5. 4 four
6. 3 three
7. 2 two
8. 7 seven
9. 9 nine
FLOWER FUN

Page 8
1. 2 + 2 = 4
2. 3 + 4 = 7
3. 1 + 5 = 6
4. 3 + 3 = 6

Page 9
1. 3 + 2 = 5
2. 2 + 1 = 3
3. 1 + 4 = 5

Page 10
1. 7
2. 6
3. 8
4. 4

Page 11
1. 2
2. 8
3. 3
4. 6

5. 6
6. 4
7. 2
8. 5

Page 12
1. 7
2. 8
3. 1
4. 6
5. 9
6. 4
7. 3
8. 2
9. 5
SUNFLOWER

Page 13
1. 5
2. 9
3. 6
4. 7
5. 9
6. 10
7. 8
8. 2

Page 14
1. 3 + 4 = 7
2. 2 + 3 = 5
3. 5 + 4 = 9
4. 5 + 2 = 7

Page 15
1. 6 blue
2. 8 yellow
3. 7 red
4. 6 blue
5. 8 yellow
6. 7 red
7. 9 brown
8. 9 brown

Page 16
1. 4 + 2 = 6
2. 1 + 1 + 1 + 1 = 4
3. 3 + 5 = 8
4. 4 + 5 = 9

Page 17

Page 18
1. 5 − 2 = 3
2. 4 − 2 = 2
3. 6 − 3 = 3
4. 3 − 2 = 1

Page 19
1. 8 − 4 = 4
2. 6 − 2 = 4
3. 5 − 3 = 2
4. 7 − 4 = 3

Page 20
1. 6
2. 1
3. 3
4. 5
5. 2
6. 8
7. 4
8. 7

Page 21
1. 3
2. 1
3. 2
4. 6
5. 0
6. 5
7. 4
8. 1

Page 22
1. 6
2. 5
3. 4
4. 1
5. 3
6. 9
7. 0
8. 2

9. 7
DRAGONFLY

Page 23
1. 6
2. 2
3. 4
4. 5
5. 4
6. 3
7. 0
8. 1

Page 24
1. 8 − 1 = 7 − 1 = 6
2. 6 − 3 = 3 − 2 = 1
3. 5 − 0 = 5 − 3 = 2
4. 7 − 2 = 5 − 1 = 4

Page 25
1. 3
2. 6
3. 8
4. 2
5. 5
6. 7
7. 4
8. 1

Page 26
1. 8 − 4 = 4
2. 5 − 3 = 2
3. 6 − 3 = 3

Page 27
1. 4:00
2. 2:00
3. 12:00
4. 7:00

Page 28
1. 9
2. 4
3. 5
4. 3
5. 8

Page 29
1. 3
2. 3 (color the butterfly)
3. 5
4. 4
5. 0
6. 8
7. 6
8. 6 (color the butterfly)

Page 30

Page 31
1. 5
2. 5
3. 3
4. 5
5. 7
6. 7
7. 6

Page 32
1. 5 + 2 = 7
2. 4 + 4 = 8
3. 6 − 1 − 1 = 4

Page 33
1. 6 − 3 = 3 + 2 = 5
2. 8 − 4 = 4 − 2 = 2
3. 3 + 6 = 9 − 5 = 4
4. 5 + 2 = 7 − 1 = 6

Page 34
1. 9
2. 6
3. 8
4. 6
5. 7
6. 8